Izzy had already run out of sight again, and as he drove, Jon couldn't help wishing that Rose was here with him. She had always helped him out in all his farm emergencies – surely she'd be much better able to track Izzy down than him? He made a decision – he was going to get her. Jon turned the car round and drove quickly back to the farm. He pulled up in the yard and leaned out of the window, calling, "Rosie! Come on, girl! We've got a job to do."

ROSE
& IZZY

The Cheekiest Dogs on the Farm

Based on the story by JON KATZ

Adapted for young readers by Ruth Knowles

RED FOX

ROSE AND IZZY: THE CHEEKIEST
DOGS ON THE FARM

A RED FOX BOOK: 978 1 849 41278 0
Published in Great Britain by Red Fox Books,
an imprint of Random House Children's Books
A Random House Group Company

This edition published 2010

1 3 5 7 9 10 8 6 4 2

Copyright © Jon Katz, 2010

Adapted for younger readers from *Saving Izzy: The Abandoned Dog Who
Stole My Heart*; first published in the USA by Random House Inc, 2007;
Published in Great Britain in 2010 by Ebury Press, an imprint
of Ebury Publishing, a Random House Group Company.

The right of Jon Katz to be identified as the author of this work has been asserted
in accordance with the Copyright, Designs and Patents Act 1988.

The Random House Group Limited supports the Forest Stewardship Council
(FSC), the leading international forest certification organization. All our titles that
are printed on Greenpeace-approved FSC-certified paper carry the FSC logo. Our
paper procurement policy can be found at www.rbooks.co.uk/environment.

Mixed Sources
Product group from well-managed
forests and other controlled sources
www.fsc.org Cert no. TT-COC-2139
© 1996 Forest Stewardship Council

FSC

Set in 13/20pt Bembo by Falcon Oast Graphic Art Ltd.

Red Fox Books are published by Random House Children's Books,
61–63 Uxbridge Road, London W5 5SA

www.**kids**at**random**house.co.uk
www.**rbooks**.co.uk

Addresses for companies within The Random House Group Limited can be found
at: www.randomhouse.co.uk/offices.htm

THE RANDOM HOUSE GROUP Limited Reg. No. 954009

A CIP catalogue record for this book is available from the British Library.

Printed and bound in Great Britain by
CPI Bookmarque, Croydon, CR0 4TD

For Bruce Tracy

(God help me if the stuff he took out had stayed in.)

ABOUT THE AUTHOR

Jon Katz lives on Bedlam Farm in New York, USA, with his wife, Paula Span, and his dogs, sheep, donkeys, cat, irritable rooster Winston and three hens. He has written lots of books for adult readers and writes regular newspaper columns about dogs and about living in the country.

For further information
see www.bedlamfarm.com

ROSE & IZZY

The Cheekiest Dogs on the Farm

CONTENTS

CONTENTS

CHAPTER ONE

Rose vs Rupert

Life on Bedlam Farm, just outside New York in the United States of America, was always *very* busy. Jon Katz, the farmer, stretched and yawned and then rubbed his sore, aching back. His back often hurt and it was getting worse every day. But he could live with it – his farm and his animals brought him so much happiness, especially his dogs, that it made all the pain and tough times worthwhile.

Jon looked down at Rose, his faithful

little three-year-old black-and-white Border collie, and she looked back with her dark, intelligent eyes. She helped him run the farm every single day, come rain or shine, and of his three dogs, Rose was the one Jon spent the most time with. Totally loyal and totally hardworking, he couldn't run the farm without her help. "Well, girl," he said to her with a tired smile, "we've got another busy day ahead of us."

It was a sunny Sunday morning in early March and Jon and Rose were awaiting the arrival of a brand-new resident of the farm – a ram who would live in the pasture with all the female sheep. As Jon looked about he saw all the farm animals were waiting for the ram's arrival too. The donkeys were hovering by the farm gate, looking about excitedly and shuffling their hooves. Mother, the farm cat, stuck her head out of the barn, but as soon as she realized something was about to happen she disappeared again shyly. She was scared of

Rose and tended to keep out of her way most of the time! Winston, the rooster, popped his head up and looked about from side to side like a meerkat before leading all his hens down a slope out of harm's way.

Jon was never *really* sure how much his animals understood, but today it certainly seemed as though they knew exactly what was going on. Except for the sheep, that was. The sheep were just chewing peacefully around their hay feeder as usual. Jon grinned; they were totally oblivious to the fact that somebody new was about to join their family!

It was almost lunch time when a big blue truck roared up the driveway of the farm. The animals all stirred, lifting their heads towards the truck – *this was it! The new arrival was here!*

Jim and Wendy, Jon's friends who had driven the ram over to the farm, stepped out of the truck. "Morning!" Wendy called happily.

Jon smiled and waved back at Wendy, nodding at Jim. He headed over to the truck, interested to take a first look at his new animal. Rose stayed behind, standing still in the front yard, just watching, waiting. Her eyes never once left the truck.

"You'll be happy with this big guy, he'll do a really good job for you," Wendy said as she got ready to unlatch the trailer and let the ram out.

Jon was pleased, but he knew he'd need to see the ram before he made up his own mind. It was always a worry getting any new animal to settle down into life on the farm, but so far things had worked out well. He just hoped this ram would settle quickly. He watched closely as Wendy spoke softly and gently to the creature. "Come on, big guy. That's it. You can do it." She encouraged him out of the truck, slapping him softly on the back, and Jim quickly managed to slip a head collar onto him and lead him out of the trailer completely.

Now that the ram was out of the truck, Jon had a proper chance to take a good look at him. What he saw made him almost gasp out loud! He was huge!

Wendy noticed Jon's expression. "You'll be OK," she smiled. But she did have a warning for him. "Do watch him. He can be grumpy, so don't ever turn your back on him or you might get hurt."

And Jon could see what she meant. This male sheep was over 130 kilograms, and he looked as though he was going to be in charge of the place. He had shaggy, brownish wool, piercing black eyes, and a pair of very sharp-looking horns. He had clearly not enjoyed being cooped up in the truck on the way over here and was looking about aggressively and tossing his head. This was definitely not an animal to mess with!

And it looked like the animals on the farm agreed with Jon. As Wendy led the ram into the pasture and took off his head collar, the donkeys quickly moved away to stand between this big stranger and the little bleating sheep, as if they were protecting them.

Rose was the only one who didn't look scared of him. She was still watching the ram carefully, and Jon saw the concentration and determination in her eyes. There was no way she was going to let this big guy boss her about. She wanted to show him who was *really* in charge of this farm!

At that moment, Jon knew Rose could handle the new animal – just like she handled everything else that came her way. He said goodbye to Wendy and Jim and turned to look at the ram. Rupert, that's what he'd call him. He carefully opened the gate to the sheep pasture, then stood back without saying a word. Rose padded quietly over and into the pasture, her gorgeous brown eyes never once leaving the ram.

At first Rupert simply ignored Rose. He sniffed at all the sheep, introducing himself to them one at a time.

Rose crouched down, casting her eyes over the scene in front of her, and then began creeping towards Rupert. She was only about five metres away from him when he finally took notice, turning his head towards her. Jon caught his breath nervously. His little dog looked absolutely tiny up so close to the ram.

Suddenly, without warning, Rupert turned and charged, thundering towards Rose with his head down, his scary horns pointing forward. But Jon needn't have worried, not even for a second. Nippy little Rose showed no fear whatsoever. She circled back around Rupert, came up behind him before he could butt her and . . . bit his bottom. Hard! The ram gave a short, angry cry and tried to twist round and attack her. But Rose hung on tight, stopping every now and then to nip round and bite Rupert on the nose, before dashing back and grabbing hold of his bottom again! Soon the big ram was spinning round and round in circles. He looked so confused. He tossed his head from side to side in pain, and tried to get a proper look at Rose.

Eventually, Rupert realized that there was no way he was going to win this fight. The little dog was too tough for him. After struggling for a while longer, Rose let go, and the ram slunk away from her as quickly as he could into the busy flock of ewes, surrounding himself with them so Rose couldn't get at him again. Her work – for now – was done. Jon smiled. His little dog had shown this huge animal who was boss. He didn't think she'd have any problems herding him with the other sheep.

And ten minutes later, Jon saw that he'd been absolutely right. He laughed out loud as he watched Rose, very confidently and very calmly, begin to herd the flock of sheep – and Rupert – over the road and across into the meadow, following Jon's commands perfectly. Every so often Rupert would look warily over at her, as if he was checking that she was too far away to bite his bottom again. Rose stared defiantly back at him and got down into her Border collie, herding crouch, staring him straight in the eye. She had won. Rose 1, Rupert 0!

Later that day, as the sun began to set, Jon and Rose went out to prepare the farm to settle down for the night. They started to slowly usher the donkeys into the barn. As soon as Jon filled their three buckets with grain they padded in, nudging him with their warm noses to get to the food. Winston and the hens hopped into the barn too and settled on their roosts for the night. Jon set out Mother's cat food, and she cautiously entered the barn for her dinner. He checked the water buckets, then, satisfied that all his animals were happily tucked up, he called goodbye, kissed Lulu the donkey on the nose and closed the barn door.

Back in the farmyard, he glanced over at the fields in the distance. Jon could see the sheep halfway up the hill, lying down, clustered together for warmth. Rupert was once again right in the middle of them all.

Noticing the direction her master was staring in, Rose's eyes took in the sheep too, and Jon could have sworn he saw a look of satisfaction in her eyes as she noticed Rupert hiding in the middle of all the girls! Rose turned back and cast her eyes over the farm to check everything was well, just as she did every night. When she was happy, she moved over to lick Jon's hand, her signal to show that they were done.

"Good girl, Rosie," Jon said softly, patting her head. Then, with everybody settled down, the two of them headed inside. There, Jon's other dogs, pale Labradors called Pearl and Clementine, joined them and they all snuggled on the sofa together so Jon could ring his wife Paula and tell her about his day. She still had a job in the city so she didn't live on the farm all the time. But she visited as much as she could and she and Jon spoke often. Before he picked up the phone, he smiled. He had only started running this farm a few years ago, so in lots of ways he was still getting used to it. It was hard work, but it made him happy. He sighed contentedly, and settled down further into the sofa.

The Animals of Bedlam Farm

Rumsfield and Rupert – the rams.

Lots of sheep – only two of my sheep have names
– Paula, who was the first ewe I ever had
(named after my wife), and Brutus, her son.
The others all have numbers instead of names.
Number 57 is one of my favourites.

Elvis the cow – he weighs over 800 kilograms
and is huge. He can even pick me up in his
mouth!

Luna – Elvis's girlfriend. The two of them sleep
together under an apple tree.

Mother – the barn cat.

Winston – the rooster.

Lots of hens – they don't have names.

Donkeys – Mama Jeanette, Lulu, Fanny and Baby
Jesus. After my dogs, the donkeys are my
personal favourites and they love to get pats,
cuddles and scratches.

The dogs – not really farm animals, but very important in my life. Rose, a hard-working Border collie, and Pearl and Clementine, pale Labradors.

CHAPTER TWO

Three Become Four

One day, not long after the arrival of Rupert, Jon came into the house to get some writing done. He wrote lots of books about his dogs and his animals. He noticed the answering machine was flashing; somebody had called and left a message. Jon wondered if it might be Paula, just calling to say hello.

But the message wasn't from Paula. Jon recognized the woman's cheery voice immediately. It was Amy, his friend who worked as an animal-rescue helper. She knew Jon's farm was a peaceful, safe and happy place for animals, so she called from time to time, asking whether he could find a home for an animal in trouble.

Jon cared a great deal about animals and he hated to think of any being in distress, but he knew he had to be sensible. He couldn't take them all in; there wasn't space on the farm for a start, so he had to think quite carefully what his answer was going to be every time she asked.

"Hi, Jon!" called Amy's voice through the machine. "I have a couple of donkeys who need homes. I know you have some already, but is there any chance you could take one more?" Jon held his finger to the button, about to end the message. He really didn't think he had the room for any more donkeys. He'd call Amy back later and tell her. But the message continued – Amy was also asking about some Border collie puppies. "Their owner's been sick," she said. "So he's not been looking after them properly." Apparently the puppies were now being sold, and they all needed homes. "Do you want one?" Amy asked.

Jon sighed. Amy knew that dogs were absolutely his weak spot – he loved them. "There's also an older Border collie. He's about three, I think. He's the puppies' father, and he's a real character. He's never had any training at all, but he's super-friendly," her message finished.

Jon sat down to have a think about what he'd just heard. He was quite sure he couldn't take in a puppy – cute as they are – he knew he was just too busy with the farm to devote the time and energy needed to help train a young dog. He thought some of his friends would probably want to buy one, though, so he decided to put them in touch with Amy.

Over the next few days it was the older dog – the puppies' father – that stuck in Jon's mind; he couldn't stop thinking about him. Jon stopped himself getting too carried away. This would need a lot of careful thought and planning. He already had three other dogs to think about. Could he really cope with one more? A pack of four dogs would mean extra feeding, training, walking and trips to the vet – could Jon really handle another dog as well as the rest of the animals on his farm? How on earth would he control four dogs? He wondered what Paula would think.

Jon knew that if he called Amy back she would be able to persuade him to take the older dog, but he really wanted to find out more about him before agreeing. Eventually Jon rang Flo, a lady who often worked with Amy and who he was sure would know about these Border collie puppies and their father.

He was right. "The dad's called Izzy," Flo

told Jon. "And he's an absolutely gorgeous, New Zealand bred, black-and-white collie."

Jon looked out of the window at Rose, who was pacing up and down in the farmyard. *What am I doing?* he thought to himself. *I already have a dog exactly like the one Flo's describing.* But he couldn't resist. Flo told him that Izzy was a beautiful dog who was just not used to being around people. "He's loving, but kind of wild." Jon didn't need to hear any more. He knew before Flo had even finished speaking that he was hooked.

Jon decided that it would be best to meet Izzy before he made his final decision. He'd need to see whether he liked the dog, but just as importantly, Izzy would need to see if he liked Jon. The next morning he drove the half-hour to the farm where the dog lived and Flo met him there. It was beautiful. There was a lovely old farmhouse as well as acres of meadows and gardens and ponds. But the idyll was shattered as soon as Jon stepped out of the car. He immediately spotted a dog running along the fence of a compound, moving so fast you could really only see a blur of black and white!

"Izzy!" Flo yelled to try and get the dog's attention. But Izzy didn't respond at all. He just carried on his manic running up and down. Jon wondered whether this lively dog even knew his own name.

They moved a little closer, and Jon saw straight away that Flo had been exactly right in her description. Izzy was absolutely gorgeous. He was dirty and his coat was very matted, but he had bright, golden eyes and was handsome and elegant. All Border collies are naturally very intelligent animals, but it sounded as if Izzy had never been trained to use his brain herding sheep, as many Border collies do, and never had any real human love and affection. Jon wondered if the poor dog was simply going mad with boredom.

Jon felt a wave of sadness that hit without warning. A few years ago, he'd taken in another untrained Border collie called Devon. John had had a hard time with Devon at first. The dog had taken a long, long time to settle into living with Jon and learning to obey. But eventually they had become great friends and loved each other dearly. Unfortunately, just last year, Devon had died, leaving Jon terribly sad. *Am I ready to take in another Border collie and train him so soon after losing Devon?* he thought.

Jon shook his head and told himself off for being so selfish. He'd learned so much through his training and work with Devon. It made sense for him to put that experience into practice now to help another dog in need, didn't it? He might even be better at it this time. Jon didn't think he could really walk away from Izzy and leave him here to be bored for ever.

Jon wanted to get closer, so he could actually

meet Izzy properly. He and Flo nervously entered the compound where the dog was still running about. Izzy totally ignored Jon, jumping up at Flo excitedly, panting in the heat, his tongue hanging out. Then he noticed Jon and moved over to give him a quick sniff. Obviously not finding him very interesting, he moved back to Flo, licking her frantically. This didn't last long either, and soon he was off again, dashing alongside the fence. Izzy did not keep still for a second. It was as though he was so excited to finally have some attention from humans that he really didn't know how to behave.

Jon knew he had to move slowly and gently to get the dog to trust him. He called out to him, offering him a treat. Izzy now decided to pay him some attention and rushed across, ignoring the treat completely, just lying down in front of Jon and rolling over.

Jon knelt beside the dog and rubbed his tummy. Now he could get a better look at him.

Izzy's teeth and muscles and weight all seemed fine. Except for the dirty and matted coat, he really seemed to be in great condition. Jon wondered if what this dog needed most of all was love and training. He was suddenly very sure he could give Izzy both. He certainly couldn't leave the dog there running up and down the side of a fence. He was taking him back to the farm!

CHAPTER THREE

"Get That Dog!"

After he and Flo had spoken to Izzy's current owner, Jon got ready to take him back to the farm. But he soon realized that this might be the hardest step. The dog had obviously never been in a car before. From the moment Jon tried to encourage him into the back of his vehicle it became a battle of wills between them, and Izzy was very stubborn! The determined Border collie just would not go anywhere near the car, no matter how much Jon tried to coax him. Eventually, Jon decided to take the matter into his own hands. He grabbed hold of Izzy and lifted him up into the back of the car, shutting the door firmly before he could run away.

Izzy hated it! Throughout the drive home he barked loudly, and Jon looked nervously through the rearview mirror as Izzy ran manically back and forth, panting harder and harder as he got more and more stressed by being in this strange moving box.

Very relieved to have made it back home without a serious accident, Jon collected a collar and lead from inside the house and then carefully opened the car's back door. He managed to slip the collar onto the barking Izzy. "Come on, boy," he said. "The car's done with. This is it, come and check out your new home."

Izzy jumped from the car, wild-eyed and

nervous, and immediately Rose, Pearl and Clementine padded out into the yard to meet this stranger. Jon watched as his dogs calmly approached the newcomer, sniffing him and then wagging their tails in a friendly manner. But Izzy obviously wasn't ready to be friends yet. He stared at the other dogs and barked loudly, curling his lip aggressively. Rose, Pearl and Clementine didn't react, but just gave him one last sniff before padding away again. They seemed to know that Izzy needed some time and space to get used to his strange new surroundings.

Izzy's tongue was hanging out – he was thirsty after all that exercise, and being cooped up and stressed out in the car for half an hour had not helped. Jon led the dog over to the porch and gave him some water, which he gulped down thirstily, before sitting up expectantly, waiting for what was coming next. His golden eyes were staring intently at everything, taking it all in carefully.

Jon thought it would be useful to walk Izzy round the farm to get him used to his new home. Bad idea!

As soon as the two of them neared the pasture, where the sheep and donkeys were grazing, Izzy took one look at the donkeys, slipped out of his collar and ran off in a panic. He had obviously never seen a donkey before and, scared and confused, just wanted to get out of there as quickly as he could. And, wow, was he fast!

Jon was completely terrified. Izzy had disappeared out of sight. There were deep woods all around the farm where the dog could easily get himself lost, and Jon had no idea where Izzy was heading, other than away from the donkeys. Izzy had only just arrived, he had no tags or identification and the busy main road was not far away – anything could happen and Jon knew he needed to act now.

He ran back to the yard, jumped in his car and headed off in the same direction as Izzy. Jon hadn't been driving for long before he spotted a blur of black and white ahead of him on the road. Luckily there wasn't much traffic, but Jon's heart was pounding hard in his chest. He pulled over as near to the dog as he could, got out and gave chase. He managed to grab Izzy, but this only made things worse. To Jon's horror, the dog wriggled out of his grasp and dashed off into the woods, running even faster than he had before.

"Oh, no!" Jon cried loudly. He had no idea how he'd go about finding Izzy now. With his bad back, there was just no way he could catch up with the dog. He hadn't even had Izzy for an hour and he'd already lost him. *Have I been stupid for even thinking I could take on another untrained dog?* he thought. But his worries were cut off mid-flow when Izzy suddenly popped back out of the woods a few metres ahead of him on the road and carried on running. Jon breathed a sigh of relief. He leaped back into his car and resumed the chase.

But Izzy had already run out of sight again, and as he drove, Jon couldn't help wishing that Rose was here with him. She had always helped him out in all his farm emergencies – surely she'd be much better able to track Izzy down than him? He made a decision – he was going to get her. He turned the car round and drove quickly back to the farm. He pulled up in the yard and leaned out of the window, calling, "Rosie! Come on, girl! We've got a job to do."

Always obedient, Rose quickly trotted over and jumped onto the passenger seat. She looked over at Jon as if she was telling him not to worry. *I'm here now*, she seemed to be saying with her eyes. *Don't worry, we'll find that naughty little dog.* And so, back on the road with faithful Rose at his side, Jon felt much better about his chances of finding Izzy.

They drove on and on up the road, but there was no sign of the Border collie. Jon was getting more and more worried. They finally entered a little village, and Jon spotted a group of people standing waiting to meet their children off the school bus. He pulled up and shouted across to them, "Have you seen a dog running by?" They nodded and pointed up the hill. Jon called his thanks and carried on. But how long was he going to have to keep going for? He just could not believe how far Izzy had got in so short a time.

They were nearly two miles away from Bedlam Farm by the time Jon and Rose spotted Izzy again. The dog must have been really scared of the donkeys. He'd just kept running and running! Jon knew he had to approach carefully this time. He couldn't risk Izzy getting away and heading into the woods again. He managed to overtake Izzy in the car, calling his name loudly out of the window as he passed. Izzy took absolutely no notice. He was still in a panic, running flat out to get away from the strange animals on Bedlam Farm.

Jon wasn't sure what to do next. Rose barked loudly, as if she too was calling Izzy's name. Jon decided to put his trust in her. He pulled the car over, opened the door and yelled to Rose, "Get that dog!" He didn't need to say anything else. Rose knew exactly what to do. As Izzy came racing past the car she jumped down and tore after him, running just as fast as he was. She managed to grab onto the fur of his tail, startling him. And, for the first time in over two miles, the little dog's manic trance was momentarily broken. He spun round to try and shake Rose off. But she held on tight.

Rose looked over at Jon for more instructions, but he didn't need to give her any. Izzy was now exhausted by his mad dash from the farm. His sides were heaving and his tongue was dragging almost to the ground with tiredness. He didn't seem to know what to do with himself.

"Izzy," Jon called the dog's name softly. "It's OK, come here." He held out his arms as he called, and to his relief and happiness Rose let go and Izzy padded over, dropping to the ground in front of him. Jon whispered to him, patting his head and rubbing his tummy in an attempt to calm him down.

Jon took another good look at the dog. He could barely move with exhaustion and Jon realized that he was going to have to tread carefully around him. There were going to be a lot of new things for the little dog to get used to, and if Jon didn't want to be chasing him about all over the country, he'd need to be careful, and protect him as well as train him. He picked Izzy up and put him back in the car.

Instead of jumping into the passenger seat as she usually did, Rose hopped in the back with Izzy and lay down beside him for the journey back to the farm. She obviously thought this newcomer needed some looking after too.

Jon breathed a sigh of relief. He was so pleased to have Izzy back in the safe, fenced farmyard. He gave the exhausted dog some water, which he lapped up quickly before lifting his head expectantly as if to say, *More, please!* Jon smiled and went inside to refill the bowl. He could not believe his eyes when he came back outside a few moments later and saw that Izzy was gone – again.

Panicked and annoyed, Jon raced from the porch in search of the naughty dog. But he burst out laughing when he saw where Izzy had got to. The little horror had jumped the fence and was peering round the corner of the house, staring determinedly at the donkeys. Jon smiled tiredly to himself. His challenge with Izzy had really begun!

CHAPTER FOUR

CHAPTER FOUR

Jon vs Izzy

There was plenty of trouble at Bedlam Farm from that day on!

Izzy had not spent much time around people, so he was completely freaked out by lots of things other dogs would take for granted. He'd never heard the noise of the dishwasher before, for example, so he was absolutely terrified, obviously thinking it was some strange creature coming to attack him. Jon would catch him running frantically about the house to try and get away from the noise. Izzy had never gone out for a walk on a lead before, or been given a bone. There was so much to learn, for Jon as well as Izzy. But Jon knew that training was all about bonding and patience, so he kept going, speaking softly and calmly to Izzy every time a new challenge came along.

Jon was pleased to discover that he had been right that day he first met Izzy. Although there was often chaos, the little Border collie was a bright, clever dog, and in the first week or so Izzy learned a huge amount. After only a few days he was behaving like a totally different dog from the one Jon and Rose had chased up the road.

Izzy's Progress Report
Week 1

Izzy seems to be the most intelligent dog I have
  ever had. He watches, absorbs and remembers.
He has now learned to respond to his own name
  and pays attention when called.
He has learned to respond to some instructions:
  "sit", "lie down" and "stay".
Izzy seems happy to sleep in a crate now. I keep
  it near my office so Izzy sees it as a safe place,
  away from the rest of the farm.
Helped by Rose, Pearl and Clementine, he is able
  to go on walks in the woods (though he is still
  a bit manic and needs a lot more attention and
  supervision than the others!).
Knows what to do with a bone now, which is
  good as chewing bones is calming for dogs.
He is starting to become good friends with Pearl,
  Clementine and Rose. Especially with Rose, and

the two of them often sit quietly together in the yard. Each morning when he emerges from his crate, Izzy licks the other dogs to say hello. Izzy seems generally calmer. When I read or watch TV he plops down at my feet, and under the desk when I'm writing – just like Devon used to do.

He also seems to be getting used to the rest of the farm animals and no longer bolts when he sees the donkeys.

After Izzy had been with Jon on Bedlam Farm for a couple of weeks, Flo and Amy came to visit, to see how Izzy was settling into his new life. They watched, smiling as the Border collie tore around the yard playfully with Rose, before coming obediently when Jon called him.

"Wow!" Amy grinned. "Izzy hit the jackpot."

Jon smiled proudly. "So did I," he answered.

But just a few days later, Jon began to wonder if he'd got carried away with excitement over Izzy's progress too soon . . .

One morning he left Izzy secure in the yard, but when he returned half an hour later the dog had gone. Then Jon saw that Izzy's little face was staring at him from the other side of the fence! At first, Jon couldn't decide if he was angry or impressed by Izzy's determination and cleverness. *How on earth did he manage to get out?*

Jon walked quickly over to the gate by the fence. He was certain he'd locked it behind him, but maybe he was mistaken – he had been in a rush this morning, after all. But no, the gate was exactly as he had left it. Though Jon did notice a very small pile of earth by his feet. He bent down to take a look and shook his head in disbelief. The clever little dog had tunnelled under the fence so he could get out of the yard!

Jon opened the gate and called Izzy back, leading him into the house. Once he was safely back inside Jon rolled a big boulder against the hole, hoping it would block Izzy's escape route. "That should do it," he said to himself.

Jon soon discovered he was very wrong. A simple boulder wasn't going to stop Izzy!

The next day, exactly the same thing happened. Jon left the house and went out into the yard to see Izzy on the other side of the fence again. *How* is *he doing it?* Jon asked himself. He checked all around the gate and the fence, but couldn't figure it out.

He brought Izzy back into the yard and locked the gate again, making sure the boulder was in place. "Stay," he told Izzy, not expecting him to for one moment! He headed back into the house and took up his position, secretly watching Izzy through a window.

Moments later, clever Izzy used the boulder as a launch pad to help him jump straight over the fence. Jon chuckled out loud. This was impressive, but it was a serious problem. For the dog's own safety he had to stop Izzy escaping. Later that night, when Izzy was safely back in the house, Jon leaned rakes and shovels against the other side of the fence to stop Izzy seeing it as a safe escape route.

This didn't stop Izzy either: he just ploughed straight through the garden tools!

Then, a few mornings later, Jon even saw Izzy opening the chain on the gate with his teeth. This Border collie was really going to test his patience!

It wasn't just outside that Jon was having problems training Izzy. Inside the house, too, Izzy was demonstrating that he was nowhere near as settled on Bedlam Farm as Jon had hoped.

Whenever Jon went out, he left Izzy in his crate so that he couldn't get out and run round the house causing havoc. One night, Jon had been out for dinner with some friends. When he got back, he found a real mess — it looked like the house had been burgled. "Oh, no!" he said out loud, looking around to try and work out what had happened. It didn't take him long to figure it out . . . Izzy had managed to open the lock and completely demolish his crate. Once out, he'd wreaked havoc in the kitchen.

Jon called Izzy over and the dog stood in front of him, looking up with those intelligent golden eyes. However frustrating this was, Jon knew it was just another example of how clever Izzy was. But he had to make this work. He had to make Izzy understand that he had to stay where Jon told him to for his own safety.

The next day Jon bought a stronger crate for Izzy to stay in. He was sure he wouldn't be able to break his way out of this one. He was wrong again!

Izzy was fine if Jon was at home for the night, and happily stayed in his crate if Jon put him inside it. But the very next time Jon went to his friends' for dinner, he returned to find the brand-new crate burst open, flipped over and a nearby rug ripped to shreds.

It was hard to imagine that the cuddly dog who loved being by Jon's side during the daytime could be so aggressive, but that's exactly how it was. Jon realized that now Izzy had found a human who loved him and looked after him, he couldn't bear to be away from him. As soon as Jon left the house, Izzy thought that he'd been abandoned for good and got stressed out and frantic. Jon felt terrible. Izzy had been unloved for so long, it really scared him when Jon went away. But Jon couldn't be around all the time, and he knew he *had* to train Izzy to cope during those times.

CHAPTER FIVE

Well Done, Izzy!

Izzy tried to stay by Jon's side as much as he possibly could, not going anywhere unless his new master was with him – even when Jon was doing his jobs.

But there was one other person Izzy would allow to take him for a walk and that was Annie. Apart from Rose, Annie was the most important helper Jon had in running the farm. She loved animals so much, and was so good with them – always knowing exactly what they wanted or needed – that Jon jokingly called her the Farm Goddess. She was now one of the most important people in Jon's life and he found it hard to imagine Bedlam Farm without her.

Even so, Annie amazed him sometimes with the things she did – like taking a chicken home to live with her and her husband for a week when it needed to recover from an injury, and once stopping her car to check on an injured snake in the road – but he knew she only acted the way she did because she cared so much.

Because of Jon's sore back, Annie did a lot of things around the farm that he could no longer do. She worked hard and put in long hours, but she did everything with a smile on her face. And she still found the time to go out first thing in the morning and say hello to all the animals before getting on with her work. Her tasks included: hauling the hay to feed the animals, looking after the fences and gardens, taking the dogs for longer walks than Jon could manage and even shovelling out manure from the barns! When she first joined the farm, Jon had been worried that it was too much work for Annie, and that she wouldn't be able to spend as much time as she'd have liked with the animals she loved so much. But they became a great team, and things worked out brilliantly.

Jon's jobs on the farm

Buy hay
Collect eggs
Move sheep
Feed the animals
Organize shoeing and shearing
Look after all the buildings and grounds
Sell fleece and manure
Exercise, feed and train the dogs

The animals on the farm loved Annie as much as Jon did and would come rushing over as soon as they saw her, pushing their noses into her in a friendly hello. Nowadays even Izzy did this!

One Monday morning, Annie arrived for work as normal, calling "Hello!" to Jon as she came down the driveway. She did this every day – it was nothing special. Jon looked up as all four of his dogs rushed over to Annie to greet her. They always did this – this was nothing special either. But Jon could tell that today, for some reason, the dogs were behaving differently. They were much more excited than usual – even Rose – and were barking and nosing at Annie much more than they usually did.

Jon went over to investigate. At first he could see nothing out of the ordinary; then he spotted something moving in Annie's jacket pocket! A very tiny, very cute, white baby rabbit stuck its little nose out and sniffed around, before popping out the rest of its head. Jon gasped with shock and looked at his friend for an explanation.

Annie grinned at him, and pulled the little animal out of her jacket. "Isn't he gorgeous?" she asked. And Jon had to admit that he was. He was only about the size of a teacup! But Jon was worried about exactly how gorgeous – and delicious – his dogs thought this little creature was! They were barking and yapping excitedly at him.

Annie ignored them. "This is Eli," she announced. She told Jon that she'd bought the rabbit as a present for her husband, but as he was still so little, she was going to carry him around with her while she worked – until he was big enough to be left by himself.

Jon looked down again. Rose, Izzy, Pearl and Clementine were all staring intently at tiny Eli, their eyes never once leaving him. They began to circle around Annie. Jon had seen them do this many times before – to the little animals they hunted in the woods. Now he was really worried. He knew how upset Annie would be if any harm came to Eli.

He was just about to open his mouth to call the dogs inside, when Annie spoke instead. She looked down at each of the dogs in turn. "Forget it, Pearl. Rose, don't even think about it. Clem, back off, this isn't a toy. Izzy? No way!" She then gave them all a friendly pat on the head, and to Jon's total amazement, all four of the dogs calmed down immediately, trotting off happily back to what they were doing. Jon couldn't believe it. Little Eli had made it through his first meeting with Jon's dogs. Maybe Annie really was the Farm Goddess after all!

After that, Jon often saw Eli's little pink nose poking out from Annie's jacket pocket. The following week, Jon was feeding the donkeys and giving Baby Jesus a pat, when suddenly, out of the corner of his eye, he spotted a black streak rocketing past him. It was Izzy, of course. He'd managed to escape from the front yard – again. For a moment Jon wondered whether his naughty dog was chasing poor Eli and quickly rushed after him. But it wasn't the baby rabbit that Izzy wanted.

Several times over the previous weeks, when Jon had been herding the sheep with Rose, Izzy had charged into the pasture, disturbing Rose's carefully organized flock. The sheep panicked and scattered about, crashing into fences as they tried to get as far away as possible from this overexcited dog.

Jon watched now as Izzy zoomed towards the pasture once again, sneaked under the gate and made his way towards the sheep.

As soon as they spotted the Border collie, the sheep moved quickly away from him to the farthest corner of the pasture.

Jon couldn't believe it – Izzy just *had* to learn to obey him. This sort of behaviour was dangerous for him and the other animals. He charged over and opened his mouth to scream at Izzy to stop and lie down. But the sight of the Border collie running around by the sheep reminded him of Rose. He suddenly remembered that this – herding sheep – is what Border collies were good at, after all. So he stayed quiet, and decided to watch and see how Izzy handled himself. It would be interesting to see what his newest dog – who'd never had any herding training – could do.

Izzy realized Jon was nearby and he lifted his head to acknowledge him, staring intently at his owner, before looking back at the sheep again. He dropped down into the Border collie crouch and started making eye contact with the sheep. *Good sign!* Jon thought to himself. Good working dogs always control sheep with their eyes and not their teeth – he was impressed that Izzy could do so much so naturally. It only took a moment of having

Izzy stare at them before the sheep realized that this dog meant business. They huddled together, frozen to the spot.

Without any commands at all from Jon, Izzy crept slowly and confidently towards the flock. He moved to the left and then behind them. Jon couldn't believe it – this is exactly what a good herding dog should do, and somehow Izzy knew it without having ever been told! Jon resisted the temptation to shout out loud with pride. The sheep moved forward, with Izzy still behind them. After a moment, he looked over at Jon as if asking for some instructions. But Jon wasn't sure what to do – the two of them had done no training together. He had no idea what words or instructions the Border collie would actually understand – until a few weeks ago he hadn't even understood his own name. Jon hesitated for a moment, and then decided just to go for it. Izzy had been super-impressive so far. He pointed to the right – to the gate of the sheep pen, and Izzy moved towards it. So did the sheep, doing exactly as Izzy wanted. Jon was overjoyed. "The pen!" he cried to Izzy as the sheep plodded into it. "Well done! The pen!"

This was a huge achievement for Izzy and he'd just shown how controlled and clever he could be when he wanted to. It was time for training to begin!

CHAPTER SIX

Rose at Work

From then on Izzy and Jon trained often, but it was still Rose that Jon relied on for actually herding the sheep day to day. But just a few weeks later, Rose got ill. At first Jon wasn't too worried. Because his dogs were free to wander around the farm and do whatever they wanted, they often found something interesting to eat that didn't agree with their stomachs and made them sick for a couple of days. Rose was quiet, and obviously not her normal self, but she carried on herding the sheep as always. However, after a few days, she was getting no better.

One morning, after she'd been ill for three days, Jon went into the kitchen and discovered that Rose was still being sick and was now bleeding from her mouth. He grabbed his phone in a panic and immediately called the vet to tell him that he and Rose were on their way. Then he gently scooped up the little dog and put her in the car.

On the drive to the vet's Jon was so angry with himself for not taking better care of Rose, for making her work when she was ill, that he was almost in tears by the time they arrived and were shown into the vet's surgery.

The vet saw what the problem was straight away, and he spoke gently, trying to calm Jon. He told him that Rose had obviously eaten something that had bones in it. The bones were now stuck in her stomach. It sounded serious. "What can you do?" Jon asked the vet, his voice shaking.

He learned that Rose would probably need an operation to remove the bones. The vet didn't want to perform such serious surgery if he didn't absolutely have to. So he decided to keep Rose in the surgery on medication for a few days to see if he could get the bones to pass through her system by themselves.

Jon was lonely on the drive back to Bedlam Farm. Over the past three years, he had got so used to having Rose by his side for every job that he needed to do on the farm, not just herding the sheep, so now, even heading back there without her felt strange and lonely. He was relieved that – even if poor Rose did have to have the operation – the vet was going to make her better, but he was still angry with himself for ignoring the fact that Rose was ill. *Have I made her worse?* he worried.

He wondered how he was going to

manage over the next week without Rose there to help him. Izzy was doing well with his training, but he was nowhere nearly as good at it as Rose. She always made the difficult herding tasks look easy, and Jon didn't want to push Izzy with too much too soon. He couldn't put Izzy or the sheep in any kind of danger, so he decided he would leave the flock where they were while Rose was away. Instead of moving them from pasture to pasture so that they'd always have long, fresh grass to munch on as usual, he decided he would give them some hay to eat instead.

Once he'd made sure the sheep were all OK, the only thing Jon could do was keep working and throw himself into his farm jobs and his writing to stop himself constantly worrying about poor Rose. It didn't work that well, and she was constantly on his mind. Jon called the vet's office several times a day and the staff were very patient with him, keeping him updated with exactly how Rose was.

A couple of mornings later, Jon came into the house to make his regular call to the vet. Izzy, Pearl and Clementine followed him inside. All three of them had been quieter than normal. They knew Rose was missing, and they were behaving as if they were just as worried about her as Jon was. They hovered by Jon's feet as he talked on the phone. Rose was now well enough for visitors, the nurse told him: he could come and visit her if he wanted. "I need to warn you though, sir," she told him gently, "Rose hasn't been able to eat properly so we've put her on a drip to make sure she's still getting all the nutrition she needs."

The nurse made all this sound completely normal, and nothing to worry too much about, but Jon could not believe his eyes when he saw Rose in her cage at the surgery. His trusty companion, his number one helper on the farm, now looked very little, and very scared. She was surrounded by medication and tubes, and X-rays and charts. Jon reached out to stroke her soft nose through the bars of the cage. She looked back at him seriously with her big, dark eyes and concentrated hard on him. Jon shivered – he was suddenly so worried he was going to lose Rose for good, that she'd never come back to Bedlam Farm.

But Rose was a fighter, and this time she was lucky. After only four days at the vet's, Jon was allowed to bring her home. She hadn't needed to have the operation, the medicine had done the trick and the bones were gone, but she wore a bandage where the drip had been inserted, and she looked thin and very tired. "She's going to need lots of rest," the vet told Jon before he and Rose left to drive home. "Seriously, she's going to need some time off from her farm work so she can get properly better."

On the way back to the farm, Jon was thinking about how he would cope with all the jobs without Rose for even more days, so that she could take the rest she needed, when his phone rang, interrupting his thoughts.

He pulled the car over and looked at the screen. It was his friend Peter, another farmer who lived nearby. Jon answered the call, stroking Rose's head as she lay on the seat next to him. Peter was very flustered. "I've got a crisis," he said urgently. He told Jon that lots of his new cows had escaped from their barn during the night. Peter and one of his neighbours had managed to round up most of them but two of the cows were still on the loose, wandering up a very busy road.

Jon knew how dangerous this was for passers-by, as well as for the cows. "Can I do anything to help?" he asked his friend.

There was a moment's silence on the other end of the phone. "Actually," Peter said hesitantly, "that's why I'm calling really . . . I don't think I can get these guys back without help. Do you think Rose could do it?"

Jon told Peter he'd think about it and put down the phone. He didn't know what to do for the best. Rose was famous around the area for her amazing herding skills. Jon knew that losing cows was a very big deal and he wanted to help his friend, but Rose was just recovering from a very serious illness and she needed some rest. Jon was worried he'd overstretch her before she'd even got back home. He wanted her to get better, not worse.

He looked at the little dog on the seat beside him. She lifted her head and looked expectantly at him, as if asking, *What?*

Jon decided to let Rose make the decision for herself. "Do you want to go to work, Rosie?" he asked her carefully. Immediately, the Border collie's head swivelled round to face him properly and her eyes brightened.

She sat up. Jon didn't need to say anything else. They drove over to Peter's farm. Help was on the way!

When they got close, Jon saw the two cows dashing around in panicked circles. Various people – including Peter – were running about waving at them, trying their hardest to direct the big animals into Peter's waiting trailer.

Jon pulled into the nearest pasture, opened the car door and let Rose out. He pointed over at the cows, saying nothing. Rose stared him straight in the eye and moved her head slightly, almost as if she was nodding in understanding. Then she charged – straight through the fields towards the escaped cows. Rose circled behind them, just as she did when herding sheep, and then pushed the two cows towards the trailer. They scrambled aboard. And all the people gathered about clapped and cheered.

Jon smiled to himself. He was so proud. The whole thing hadn't taken Rose more than five minutes. "And now," he said as Rose padded back to his side, "let's go and get you some rest!"

CHAPTER SEVEN

Perfect Pearl

Although it was Rose whom Jon relied on more than the other dogs, and Izzy who was taking up most of his time at the moment, it was Pearl, one of his two Labradors, whom John often treated extra-specially. Pearl was the only one of his dogs he allowed to stay outside the fences if she wanted to. That was because Jon knew she wouldn't chase anything or wander off. He never kept Pearl in a crate indoors, either. She didn't raid the rubbish bin or chew anything she shouldn't, so he never needed to. Pearl really was his most well-behaved dog. She was an old dog now, and had had many operations on her legs. The vet called her "Perfect Pearl" because of how easy she was to deal with, and in Jon's eyes, she was perfect.

Jon often went to a physical therapy centre – a place where he could get treatment for his back. The therapists and nurses there all loved dogs, so Jon sometimes took Pearl and his other Labrador, Clementine, with him to cheer up the staff while they worked.

Pearl, especially, fitted in brilliantly on her visits to the centre. Jon always knew where she was, even if he couldn't see her, by the *oohs* and *ahhs* he could hear from everybody she passed. Soon Jon started taking her with him every week. As soon as they entered the building together the staff would greet them with, "Hey, Pearl!" often just giving Jon a quick nod hello in their rush to pat Pearl or give her a treat.

One day, just a week or so after Rose came back to the farm, Jon and Pearl went to Jon's treatment session. While they were there, Jon spotted a lady in a wheelchair struggling to stand up. Although she looked as if she was in a lot of pain, her forehead creased up with concentration, she was still smiling.

Pearl seemed to spot her at exactly the same time, and she trotted over, tail wagging, and rested her head on the lady's lap.

Jon immediately went to call Pearl back – she was never normally so forward with people she didn't know. But the lady grinned, pleased by Pearl's attention. "What a beautiful creature you are," she told the Labrador. "You're here to help me get up, aren't you?" She looked over at Jon. "I'm Adelaide," she said. She told him that she was suffering from arthritis, which meant it was very difficult for her to move around. Jon introduced himself and Pearl, and then looked on as his dog stared up into Adelaide's eyes. With Pearl watching her closely, the lady finally managed to get herself up out of her chair and onto a bed. Jon couldn't help but think that Pearl had helped her in some way, maybe giving her the energy she needed.

After that, every time they went to the clinic, Jon noticed that Pearl and Adelaide had a special bond. Pearl would head over to the old lady as soon as she saw her. Every time, Adelaide would ask, "How am I doing, girl?" and Pearl would wag her tail in response.

And Pearl *did* seem to be helping Adelaide. It was almost as though Pearl understood what the old lady was going through in her struggle to move because Pearl had had so many operations on her own legs. After Adelaide had done her exercises, Pearl would curl up next to her, and stay absolutely still while the lady stroked her head and chest.

Abi, one of the therapists at the centre, said she never saw Adelaide happier than when Pearl was around.

And Adelaide agreed. "She's my vitamin," she would always say with a smile!

"I so miss having a dog," Adelaide told Jon one day as they sat quietly talking while Pearl rested her head in the old lady's lap. "But I had to let my dog go and live with my cousin as I couldn't walk her or give her everything she needed any more. She was a black Labrador."

Jon felt a wave of sadness for his new friend. He knew how he'd feel if he had to give up Pearl and he thought Adelaide must be lonely living by herself. He mentioned the way he felt to Abi.

She shook her head sadly. "I know," she responded. "Everybody here is really worried about her. We're not sure she should really live on her own any more. She's so stubborn though!" Abi told Jon that she – and lots of other people – had suggested that Adelaide go and live with her family, or move into some sort of old people's home, but every time it was mentioned, Adelaide said that there was no way she would leave the home she knew and loved.

So when Adelaide's course of therapy sessions were over, the old lady said goodbye to everybody at the centre, insisting she would be totally fine by herself. She came to say goodbye to Jon and Pearl, and he could see tears in her eyes. She was obviously going to miss Pearl so much. Jon decided they should go and visit her some time.

Adelaide loved the idea. "That would be so wonderful," she said softly.

The next week, armed with biscuits, books, fruit and Pearl, Jon drove over to Adelaide's house. He couldn't believe his eyes when he pulled up. Her house was old, and very, very neglected – it needed a *lot* of work doing to it. Paint was peeling off, the garden was full of weeds and the roof was cracking. Jon took a deep breath as he knocked on the door with Pearl at his side. He wondered what it would look like inside.

But when Adelaide called them in, Jon was relieved to find that things were much neater and cleaner than he had feared. There was a big photo in the living room of a younger Adelaide with her much-missed black Lab. It made Jon's heart ache for the lonely old lady.

As soon as she heard her friend's voice again, Pearl padded over to the sofa and struggled up on her sore legs to lie down next to Adelaide. She put her head in the old lady's lap, and within minutes was snoring away!

Jon didn't want to over-tire Adelaide – she was not a well woman, after all – but he went back as often as he could over the next few weeks, always taking food and flowers and pictures of his dogs and other animals for her to look at. Every time Pearl would trot straight into Adelaide's house and curl up beside her.

Sometimes Jon would leave Pearl with Adelaide while he went for his appointment at the therapy centre or ran some other errands. He always found them resting together when he returned!

One day, at the start of April, Jon got a shock when he went for his weekly visit. He knocked at Adelaide's door as usual, but there was nobody at home – she wasn't there! His heart began to beat faster and he started to panic. *What if she's fallen somewhere and can't get up?* He peered through the windows but couldn't see anything unusual, and Pearl barked loudly – she was just as worried as he was.

After a few minutes a neighbour came over from her house next door. "Adelaide's been taken into hospital," she called. "She had a fall." She gave Jon the phone number of Adelaide's daughter so he could find out what was going on.

Jon worried about the old lady all the next day. He decided he should call and find out if his friend was OK. Adelaide's daughter answered quickly. "Ah! I've heard so much about you and Pearl," she said in a friendly voice. She explained that her mother was doing well and would be coming out of hospital the next day. "She's desperate to see Pearl," she told him.

Jon was relieved to hear Adelaide would be able to come back to the home she loved so much, but he waited a couple of days to let her settle back in before going over. But when he and Pearl got there he saw the flashing lights of an ambulance waiting outside, and Adelaide was strapped onto a stretcher, about to be wheeled into it. Jon and Pearl rushed over.

Adelaide waved and winked, trying to

look as cheerful as she could. "I've finally agreed to leave," she told Jon sadly. She was moving to a home many miles away. He didn't know what to say – he knew what a big deal this was for her. He simply squeezed her hand.

Pearl seemed to realize how sad she was too. She padded over, looking puzzled, and rested her head on the lady's shoulder. She followed, her tail wagging, as the men wheeled Adelaide into the ambulance and watched intently with her big brown eyes as she saw her friend for the last time. Adelaide waved, and Pearl barked as the ambulance drove away.

"Let's go, girl," Jon said sadly, gently stroking Pearl's head. They got into the car and drove back to the farm in silence. Pearl seemed to understand perfectly that she wasn't going to see much of her friend again. But Jon took comfort from knowing how happy getting to know Pearl had made Adelaide. With those beautiful warm eyes, and her loving, gentle personality, his special dog had made an old woman very happy.

CHAPTER EIGHT

Happy Easter!

Now, finally, life on Bedlam Farm was getting back to normal. Izzy was settling down, Rose was fit and well again, and Pearl and Clementine were as loving and happy as ever. The days were getting sunnier, and generally things were peaceful and calm . . . but not today!

It was Easter Sunday. The morning was bright and crisp and calm, but inside the farmhouse things were very different! Every year at Easter time, Jon – with Rose's help, of course – would take his sheep down to a meadow that looked out onto a big old brick church. All the people leaving after the Easter Sunday service would look up and wave at Jon and Rose and the sheep, and it had become something of a tradition for the locals.

Jon woke up and went downstairs cheerfully. He was looking forward to his Easter outing, but he was in for a shock. The kitchen, where the dogs slept, smelled terrible and there was a horrible mess. "Oh, no!" he said out loud. "Poor girls." Clementine and Pearl must have eaten something nasty yesterday, and it had made them sick during the night. Holding his nose and trying not to look too closely, Jon spent a long time cleaning up after them. This finally done, he put all the cloths he'd used into the washing machine, gave his dogs some food and water and then headed outside to check on the rest of the farm's animals.

The donkeys were always the first to amble over and say hello to Jon when he went out in the mornings. But today, as they headed towards him, he noticed that Lulu was limping. Jon sighed: he'd thought the drama was over for the day but obviously not. He wondered if Lulu had got something stuck in her hoof. That would be very painful for her and he needed to get it out as quickly as possible. He fetched his tool kit and took out the hoof pick, then knelt down next to Lulu and gently persuaded her to lift up her hoof so he could take a look. Jon immediately saw that he'd been right – there was a big shard of rock wedged in her hoof. He winced – it must be hurting her a lot. "Don't worry, girl," he told the donkey gently, "we'll get that nasty fellow out of there. Don't you worry." He stroked her on her soft nose, and then, as carefully as he could, set about pulling the piece of rock from her foot. Lulu was so patient and well-behaved throughout the whole thing, and she just looked at Jon with her big eyes, trusting him completely to make her better.

"That's it!" he told Lulu, holding up the rock to show her. The donkey put down her hoof and patted the ground a few times, testing to see whether or not it still hurt. Jon was smiling at her when suddenly he was knocked to the ground. "Ouch!" he cried. He had been concentrating so hard on Lulu that he hadn't noticed Rupert sneaking up behind him – he'd forgotten Wendy's warning the day the huge ram had arrived. Rupert had butted him really hard. Jon knew that he had only been trying to be friendly, but he was so heavy that it was very painful – and he'd managed to hit him right on his sore back.

Jon struggled to his feet and went to feed the animals, but as he hobbled back into the farmhouse to get ready to take the sheep over to the church, he felt sad. Paula and his daughter Emma were both busy working; they hadn't been able to come and spend Easter on the farm and Jon missed them. His busy morning and now his sore back had made him miserable, and suddenly he was feeling very sorry for himself.

But as Jon reached the door to the house, all four dogs padded out to meet him, rubbing themselves up against his legs and barking excitedly. They were so pleased to see him that he smiled, his sadness gone. Pearl had completely stolen his heart with her loving nature, Rose was his hard-working hero, Izzy was proving to be a real charmer and Clementine was quite simply the happiest dog he had ever known. They were part of his family too and he loved them. Paula and Emma couldn't be here today, but the sun was out and he had his dogs – Jon suddenly realized how lucky he was. He patted them all, one at a time, and headed indoors.

Jon got ready and called Rose to his side. They were just about to leave when Pearl trotted over and stopped right in front of them, staring up at Jon with her enormous sad eyes. *I want to come too*, she seemed to be saying. *Don't leave me here again.* Because of her sore legs, and the many operations she'd had on them, Pearl couldn't go on long walks and Jon didn't often take her very far. But today, he couldn't resist. The meadow wasn't too far away, so he decided to take Pearl with him as well as Rose. He was sure she'd be fine. "OK," he told Pearl. "Let's do it!" and she barked excitedly as if she was saying, *Thank you!*

And so the three of them headed slowly across the meadow, with Rose determinedly driving the sheep. She marched them forward calmly, and soon they were in the middle of the newly green meadow. The sun and wind of spring had cleared up all the winter mud and muck, and everything looked beautiful. They were so close to the church now that Jon could hear the muffled sound of organ music being played. "Rose, hold them," he instructed the collie, and she obeyed immediately, lying down with the flock of sheep in the middle of the meadow. She had complete control over them!

Knowing his sheep were safe under Rose's watchful eye, Jon lay back on a rock in the sun, exhausted already from his busy morning, and daydreamed. Pearl was tired out by her short walk, so she padded slowly over and collapsed onto Jon's lap to do the same. He held her close and kissed her soft nose and the two of them lay there happily together in the sun.

Suddenly, their doze was interrupted as organ music swelled out across the countryside and the church doors opened below them. Crowds of people piled out of the church, heading for their cars so they could get home to spend the rest of Easter Sunday with their families. A group of children spotted Jon, his dogs and the sheep first, making all the people below look up towards the meadow. "Hi, Jon! Hi, Rose!" the children yelled. Jon grinned. Everybody in town seemed to know Rose's name! When he met people during the rest of the year, they would always ask how she was, and whether they'd get to see her again at Easter.

He squeezed Pearl and got to his feet. Without him having to say anything, Rose knew this meant she should get to work — and she did! She marched the sheep neatly up and down the meadow so that all the people at the church could get a good look at them, and at Rose, hard at work. Every so often, she would quickly take an eye off the sheep and look at Jon for approval. He nodded at her happily. "Good girl, Rosie," he told her, and she lifted her head as if she was proud, enjoying the adulation of the audience below her.

Jon was proud too – of Rose, but also of Pearl, who stayed quiet even though she was nervously staring at the people below, and of Clementine and Izzy back home and all his farm animals.

It was nice for Jon to get some peace and quiet up here in the meadow as his days on the farm were always super-busy.

A typical day
for Jon on the farm

Get up at 5 a.m. Normally one of the dogs
   has sneaked out and eaten something that
   didn't agree with them, so I clean up after
   them.
A quick walk for the dogs.
Feed the animals – Rose and I go out and put
   some bales of hay into the hay feeder for the
   sheep and donkeys and make sure the water
   tubs are full. We put out some cat food for
   Mother, cookies for the donkeys, an apple for
   Elvis and feed for the chickens.
Feed the dogs.
Move logs to make sure there are some for the
   fire.
Breakfast for me!
Separate herding lessons for Rose and Izzy.
Let the dogs into the yard and go into the office

to try and get some writing done. Izzy and
  Pearl sleep nearby.
Have a stroll in the woods with the dogs; they do
  some ball-chasing.
Head into the pasture with Rose to move the
  animals around to ensure they get enough
  grazing.
The vet is normally here at least once a week
  checking on one animal or another.
Head off in the car on errands or to get
  groceries.
Feed dogs and then have a final walk.
Repeat the animal chores and settle them in for
  the night.

CHAPTER NINE

Controlling Your Temper

The trip across the meadow on Easter Sunday showed how well Rose knew the sheep and how good she was at controlling them, but Jon could see that Izzy's herding skills were not improving as quickly as he'd hoped. When Izzy practised with Rose and had her to copy, he did well, but he was still finding things tricky when he was by himself in his training sessions with Jon.

Jon had put a training pen in the middle of

the pasture for Izzy to practise in so that he could learn all the commands without getting too close to the sheep until he understood them properly.

Today they were working on the commands that would help Izzy herd the sheep, rather than just *chase* them. Izzy was supposed to obey the instructions "Come bye" and "Away to me", but he wasn't obeying them at all!

After about half an hour, Jon's throat ached from shouting the commands. Izzy seemed to have mastered them just a couple of days earlier, but today he was just too over-excited. He didn't want to do what Jon wanted him to do, and now they were both getting frustrated.

As Jon watched Izzy chasing the sheep wildly with an excited look in his eyes, he was suddenly very aware that although his Border collie was a very loving pet and settling in well on Bedlam Farm, Izzy was at heart a hunting dog. His instinct was actually to hunt the sheep down and devour them, not move them around a field to help a human. Jon knew they had a lot of very boring, very repetitive work to do to try and override Izzy's natural instincts. They needed to work not just on the commands, but on movement, hand signals and whistles – and it was all very difficult!

Jon took a deep breath and tried again. "Come bye," he yelled impatiently. But Izzy stayed on the opposite side of the training pen to Jon, running in excited circles. Suddenly Jon had had enough. He banged his walking stick hard on the pen's metal gate to get his dog's attention. Izzy was startled by the clang of metal and he jumped back. He was paying attention to Jon now, staring hard at him, but he still hadn't obeyed his command. This, for some reason, made Jon even more angry. "Listen to me!" he yelled at the Border collie. "Come bye. *NOW!*"

Izzy stood stock still and lifted his head, but he now just looked even more confused. Jon couldn't believe it – Izzy knew what these words meant. What was his problem? He shouted at Izzy to lie down, and the dog obeyed immediately. "There, you see!" Jon cried. "You do understand me, so what's wrong?"

At this moment, Annie happened to pass the pasture. She was carrying a bucket and was obviously on her way to fill up the water for the donkeys. "You see that?" Jon asked her, throwing up his hands impatiently. "What's wrong with him?"

Annie stared back at him and said, quietly but honestly, "What's wrong with *you?*"

For a moment Jon was stunned. "What do you mean?" he asked.

"You're edgy and angry and you're yelling at him," Annie told him firmly. "Izzy's picking up on your anger and it's freaking him out."

Jon's jaw dropped open. He knew Annie

was absolutely right, and what she was saying made him ashamed of himself. He put up a hand to his forehead and found it was sweaty. He sighed – he was hot and tense and angry, and his back hurt. And he realized with shame that he had been taking all these things out on poor Izzy.

He thought back over all their training sessions, not just today's, and he realized that Izzy was still getting over his previous life. As soon as Jon looked at him crossly or raised his voice to shout out a command, Izzy froze and backed away from him. Jon shook his head, annoyed with himself. *Why haven't I figured this out before?* he thought. He *had* to learn to control his temper, or he and Izzy weren't going to get anywhere with their sheep herding.

Jon left the pasture and Annie behind, and went to sit on the stone steps leading up to the back door of the house. Izzy followed him, padding over and crawling into his lap.

Jon bent his head and kissed the dog on the nose and then gave him a treat from his pocket. "I'm sorry, Iz," he said, feeling terrible.

But Izzy seemed to already have forgiven his owner. He wriggled further into Jon's arms, before flopping over happily to have his tummy rubbed.

"I love you to death," Jon told Izzy. "I'll try to do better, to be the human you deserve."

Izzy stared at him intently, seeming to understand every word. He licked his face gently, as if to say, *I understand and I'm going to try too.*

When Jon stood up, Izzy spun around on the spot, showing he was ready to get back to work. Jon looked down and Izzy seemed to nod his head – he wanted to try again! So the two of them walked happily back to the training pen to have another go at some herding.

Jon let Izzy into the pen and then took a

deep breath, making sure he was chilled out and relaxed before he called a command to make Izzy move to the right. Izzy obeyed immediately!

Jon whooped for joy. "Good! Good!" And Izzy loved the praise. Gone was the naughty dog who had been running around the sheep in circles, yapping loudly. Izzy now held his dark head proudly, obeying Jon's commands over and over again, showing that when he wanted to, he had just as much control as Rose did.

Annie came back, and watched in silence for a while. When Jon looked at her he saw that she was stunned. "I can't believe that's the same dog I just saw . . . or the same person."

And Jon agreed. He knew then what he should have known all along: that anger does not work — not with dogs or with humans. And it certainly wasn't going to work with Izzy . . .

CHAPTER TEN

No Work to Do

The farm was always chaotic during the spring, but this year especially, things were very hectic. As well as the general running of things, the barn was being repaired and there were bits of wood, doors and building materials scattered all over the place, and people coming and going.

Because of this, Jon wasn't surprised when, one morning on his way out to the farm, he spotted that one of the gates to the pasture had been opened and not shut properly.

He soon began to worry though when he realized that the donkeys and the sheep had escaped through the open gate and had made it by themselves across the road to the other pasture opposite the farmhouse.

Jon's heart was pounding, imagining scenes of disaster as his animals wandered about the roads. "Rosie!" he called immediately – and his loyal, hard-working little dog came running. Rose seemed to know straight away where the naughty sheep had got to, and she went dashing for the meadow.

Rose was more frantic than Jon had ever seen her, running so quickly that she became a black-and-white blur. Jon followed as fast as his sore back would allow him to, less panicked now that he knew Rose was on the sheep's case!

When he finally caught up with her, he saw that all the sheep and donkeys were now spread out, munching happily on the grass. Despite all the panic, they looked so peaceful that he decided to leave them where they were, and let them eat for a little longer before heading back.

He called Rose to his side and stroked her head gently as they watched the sheep and the donkeys chomp away happily. "What would I do without you, girl?" he asked her affectionately.

After he thought the animals had had their fill of the longer grass out here, Jon and Rose moved them back to where they were supposed to be, and he carefully shut the gate behind them. As he did so, Jon realized he could hear a sound in the distance, and he looked up, straining to work out what it was. It sounded like a whine, and he headed towards it quickly, wondering if one of his other animals was hurt or in pain.

As he got closer, he spotted Clementine in the distance: she was indeed whining loudly from her position in the yard. At first Jon wondered if she was injured, and he rushed over to check her out. But when he thought back over the past few weeks, he realized that his loving, beautiful Labrador had been miserable lately – showing it when he had gone out with one of the other dogs and left her behind. Just a few days ago when he had taken Pearl with him in the car to one of his book signings, Clementine had sat in the yard and yapped loudly, staring up at him with her sweet face. He realized that she had wanted to go out to the pasture with him and Rose today too.

He stroked her head and rubbed her tummy, and Clementine did start to calm down, but Jon couldn't help wonder – was he making her happy? That whine had sounded so terribly miserable. Was lovely Clementine no longer happy with him?

Jon sat with her in the sunshine for a

You might like these photographs of Jon's dogs and the animals of Bedlam Farm.

Enjoy looking through them!

while, thinking hard. Did he have the space in his life to look after four dogs and keep them all as happy as they should be? If today was anything to go by, the answer was no. Had Izzy's arrival and the time they were spending training together meant that he was now neglecting to spend the time he needed with Clem?

Over the next few days, whenever he caught sight of his gorgeous Labrador, Jon ran these thoughts through his mind. As sad as it made him, he began to wonder if he should let Clem go to somebody who could make her as happy as she deserved. She was so loving and affectionate and could give so much to her owner. Could she love somebody else and be happier than she was now? Jon felt terrible, but he knew he had to do what was best for her – none of this was because he didn't love her, but because he loved her so much.

Clementine profile

A well-bred Labrador. Happy, sociable and loving. Probably the most loving dog I have ever had – she sleeps with her head on my shoulder.

Loves food! Especially a piece of hamburger or some biscuits! She will even happily sit through a check-up at the vet's just because she could see the jar of treats in front of her!

Technically a hunting dog, but prefers lazing in the sun. She will occasionally chase a small chipmunk just to show Rose and Izzy that she can.

Likes chasing balls. She has real stamina and focus, runs far, always gets her ball and brings it back without fail.

Loves all things messy! Often rolls in manure just for the fun of it!

Jon had got Clementine when she was a puppy and had first seen her just after she was born. And she had changed him. When he looked at her he smiled, and he could swear that she always smiled back. Jon felt like he'd worked too hard to pick her and train to let her go.

But all his other dogs seemed to have a role in Jon's life and on the farm that Clem didn't have. Izzy, since he'd exploded into Jon's life like a bomb, was going to be an excellent sheepdog. Rose was the lead farm dog and Pearl was a house dog: her bad legs meant that she loved her quiet, peaceful life. But Clem was supposed to be a working dog, just as Rose was, and on Bedlam Farm she just didn't have any work to do.

CHAPTER ELEVEN

The Best of Both Worlds

Whether or not staying with him on Bedlam Farm was the best thing for Clementine was on Jon's mind often over the next few days and weeks.

One day he was at the therapy centre, having his back treated by Abi, when she mentioned that she was thinking about getting a dog. She knew that Jon had had a lot of experience with dogs and she asked him what breed he thought she should look at. "I want a dog who loves people, and is happy to settle down at night with me and chill out, as well as being active," Abi told him.

Suddenly a trigger went off in Jon's head. *Clementine!* Abi was young, athletic, she lived close to some trails and woods and she would even be able to bring her dog to work with her if she wanted. Could Abi be the answer to Jon's problem with Clementine?

Jon didn't mention his plan to Abi immediately: he needed to think about it, and talk it through with Paula – Clementine was, after all, Paula's favourite dog. But he did begin taking Clementine to his therapy sessions every week so that she and Abi could get to know each other and he could see how they got on together.

Of course, they got on brilliantly. Clementine was so loving and Abi so happy and gentle that they made a great pair. Jon still hadn't mentioned his plan to Abi, but after some time, he decided to move things along.

One day he was at the centre being treated, and was watching Abi and Clementine play together. "Are you still looking for a dog?" he asked Abi.

"Yep," she answered, "and I've been to look at a few, but I've not fallen in love with any of them yet. A girl just like Clem would be perfect."

Jon smiled to himself. It seemed his plan could be working even better than he had hoped. "Why don't you take Clem home with you for a weekend, or something," he suggested to her. "Then you could see what having a dog would really be like, and it might help you make up your mind." Abi loved the idea and they arranged it for the following weekend.

But as the time drew nearer, Jon began to get nervous. Had he made the right decision? He wanted to do what was best for Clementine, but he didn't want to confuse her. What if she was puzzled by suddenly being in a strange place with Abi? And selfishly, Jon was worried for himself: how would he cope without sweet, enthusiastic Clementine waking him every day? He knew he had to keep thinking about what was best for his dog, though, so the following Saturday morning, he dropped Clementine off with Abi, along with a huge bag of chews, toys, dog food and treats, and a very long list of instructions, then he took a deep breath and drove away, forcing himself not to look back. "She'll be fine. She'll be fine," he kept telling himself on the drive home.

But he couldn't help being nervous, and after a few hours he decided to call and check that everything was going OK. There was no answer, so after half an hour Jon called again. And again. He worked himself up into a panic – what if Clementine *had* been confused by being at Abi's and run off into the woods and got herself lost? What if . . . ?

But finally Abi called back. She sounded

very, very happy and was bubbling over with excitement. "What a great dog. Clem's so sweet and well-trained." She and Clementine were worn out though, Abi told him. They had chased a ball in and out of the pond and gone for a long walk through the woods. Then Abi had taken Clementine with her to her football game. "People took turns sitting with her . . . She made a million friends!" she said happily. "Everybody there wanted to pat and talk to her – Clem didn't want to leave!"

Jon had been in such a panic that something bad had happened that he had worked out a whole speech about what Abi needed to do to calm Clementine down. But she didn't need any of his advice now. Abi had done everything Jon had recommended – even microwaving a burger to give Clementine with her dinner – and things were going really well.

★ ★ ★

When Jon put down the phone, he sat alone on the sofa and had a good think about what would be the best thing for Clementine. He'd missed his loving Labrador much more than he thought he would – and she'd only been gone for a day! But he also knew that Abi was crazy about her and could give his dog all the one-on-one attention and outdoor physical exercise that he couldn't.

He sat for some time mulling everything over before he suddenly had a brainwave. *Maybe he and Abi could share Clem.* That way, they'd both enjoy having Clementine in their lives and get to spend time with her, but she would still have everything she needed. This was a hard decision, but he no longer felt as tense as he had all day. He was sure this was the right thing to do for the dog he loved so much . . .

And Abi agreed! When Jon picked up Clementine the next day, he discussed his idea with her. She couldn't stop smiling! "Clem is the dog I've been dreaming of," she told him, "but I wouldn't want to take her away from you, so this just seems perfect. If you're sure?" Jon *was* sure. And Clementine seemed sure too. She was excited to see Jon and jumped up at him barking "Hello" excitedly, but she also seemed sad to be leaving Abi behind, looking back at her from the car window with big eyes. *From now on*, Jon thought to himself. *Clem'll have the best of both worlds!*

CHAPTER TWELVE

Visitors to the Farm

One day, not long after Clementine had started splitting her time between Bedlam Farm and Abi's house, Jon got a letter. It was from a woman called Margaret who lived quite close, just a few miles away. Margaret was going to have a small group of very old friends to stay with her soon: all of them were dog lovers and all of them had read and enjoyed Jon's books. Margaret's letter said that they'd love to meet Jon, and come over and see

Bedlam Farm and all the animals they had read about.

Jon was honoured that these women wanted to come and see him: he was proud of his animals and his farm, and he found himself quite excited by the idea of showing it off to Margaret and her friends. He called her, and they arranged a visit for a day in June when Jon knew Clementine would be at the farm too. Then he set about planning an interesting day at Bedlam Farm for the ladies.

He was confident that all his dogs would make a good impression on the visitors. Jon looked down at Izzy, who was walking peacefully by his side without a lead. With a grin, he remembered the frantic dog that had arrived at Bedlam Farm a few months before, not knowing his own name and escaping up the road on his first day. Jon just couldn't believe the change in him in such a short space of time. He was calm, loving and had settled in well.

10.30 _ Introduce the dogs, and show the ladies around the dog room and living room in the house.

11.00 _ Walk out and meet the donkeys. Give them some carrots and cookies.

11.15 _ Go to the barn and see the work being done there.

11.30 _ Meet Elvis and Luna.

11.45 _ Herding demonstration by Rose and Izzy.

12.15 _ Sit on the porch and rest and have juice.

12.45 _ Head into town for lunch.

Izzy and the other Bedlam Farm dogs were friends now too. His arrival hadn't changed Rose's life much; she got on with her work and her life no matter what was thrown at her, so she accepted Izzy peacefully. Pearl and Clementine were naturally more loving and affectionate than Rose and they had almost immediately grown to love their new playmate. The three of them would often doze happily next to each other and Jon would even see Clementine gently licking Izzy's face.

And so, on a glorious day in the middle of June, bang on time, a car drove up the driveway to Bedlam Farm and Margaret and her friends climbed out, ready to meet Jon and his happy dogs. Jon could see that they were elderly ladies, all of them probably about seventy or eighty, and they were carrying some carrots for the donkeys and some biscuits for the dogs.

The dogs were as friendly as ever,

immediately padding over. Rose woofed politely to say hello, but Izzy, Pearl and Clementine rushed excitedly to the fence to greet the ladies, their tails wagging. Jon smiled. His dogs knew how to make friends and charm people, and already Margaret and her friends were cooing over them, patting and stroking them all. The dogs loved it!

At first, the women stuck to Jon's timetable, and after showing them the house, he led them over to meet the donkeys. The donkeys were always affectionate and good with people – even strangers – and Margaret and her friends loved them, especially Baby Jesus, whom the visitors all stroked and cooed over. "He's just so gorgeous!" one of them cried enthusiastically.

Then it was time for the herding demonstration. Jon looked on proudly as Rose and Izzy did their work brilliantly, calmly and confidently. The ladies were obviously impressed too: just as the final sheep was nudged into her pen by Rose, they burst into enthusiastic applause, whooping and cheering for the two Border collies. The dogs paced up and down in front of the group with their heads held proud and high – they were obviously pleased with themselves too!

Afterwards, even Rose was unusually friendly. She obviously liked their visitors and came over to the porch to give each of them in turn a quick lick before darting back off to her favourite spot in the garden where she sat so she could see everything that was going on. Izzy was on great, friendly form as well, pushing his nose into everybody's hands so he could be stroked and staring up intently with his big eyes. But, as usual, it was Pearl who was the real star of the show. She blinked and rolled over onto her back to have her tummy stroked. The ladies loved her!

Jon and his dogs sat peacefully with the

group for a while as they told him about their lives. He couldn't believe how lively they all were or how much they'd done. They met up every year without fail, and always liked to try something new. They had been hiking, canoeing, sailing, climbing and all sorts of other activities.

Suddenly Jon's phone rang, shattering the chilled-out atmosphere and the quiet chatter between Margaret and her friends. It was his friend Anthony, who helped out on the farm from time to time. Jon knew Anthony well and could tell immediately that something was not right.

"It's Mo," Anthony said. Mo was Anthony's dog, a happy, obedient black Labrador. "He's disappeared," he continued, "I've been looking and calling all over and I can't find him." Mo never ran off – he was as well-behaved as Pearl – so Jon could see why Anthony must be so worried. "I'm on my way," he told his friend. He knew he had to help – and there was only one dog he knew who was up to the challenge!

"Rose!" Jon called quickly, before apologizing to Margaret and her friends. *So much for my well-planned day*, he thought to himself. But he told the ladies to stay where they were: hopefully Rose could find Mo quickly and he would be back in time to take the ladies out to lunch as planned! Rose stood to attention at Jon's side, sharp and alert – she knew immediately that it was time to work, that there was a job needing doing.

Jon drove over to Anthony's house and let Rose out of the car. "C'mon, Rosie. Find Mo. Get Mo!" he told her, and as always, Rose seemed to understand what he wanted her to do. Full of energy, she began circling Anthony's truck. She had picked up a scent. She ran down the hill and then back again, and Jon knew that with her amazing sense of smell and hearing, Rose was getting something.

She paused for a moment and raised her ears, then charged up behind Anthony's house. She definitely seemed to be after something.

Jon followed slowly, keeping his eyes carefully on her in the distance. Suddenly he saw her frantically tearing with her teeth at some branches and weeds, barking loudly . . . Then up popped Mo. He appeared to be totally unharmed and bounded towards Jon, panting heavily. He had obviously got himself stuck in the branches and brambles, and clever Rose had found him and helped him out – once again, she had come to the rescue.

Rose joined Jon again and he bent down and kissed her on the nose. "You're my hero!" he told her, and she seemed to smile up at him.

Jon and Rose returned Mo to a very relieved Anthony and then drove straight back to the farm, where Margaret and her friends were still waiting in the sunshine. They cheered and clapped for Rose when Jon told them what she'd done and he looked on proudly as the women made a fuss of her, stroking her and giving her treats.

Later, after the ladies had left, Jon, Rose, Izzy, Pearl and Clementine headed over to the pasture together to give the farm animals their food and water for the night. The donkeys sidled over straight away. Mother the cat stuck her head out of the barn door to see who the visitors were, and Elvis and Luna watched closely from the other side of the fence. All the animals stirred at the sound of Jon's footsteps.

Jon gave them all their food and water and a pat on the head and then looked around and smiled. He was so proud of what he'd achieved on the farm and he loved all his animals so much. Once he was certain everybody was OK, he and the dogs headed inside for the night, moving together as if the five of them were one unit.

Jon sat down heavily on the sofa and sighed. *Phew! What a busy few months it has been*, he thought. New arrivals, lots of changes, and lots of hard work. Izzy and Clementine jumped up next to him on the sofa, closed their eyes and went to sleep. At his feet, Rose and Pearl did the same. Jon yawned and stretched, then, surrounded by his precious dogs, he fell asleep too.

BORDER COLLIES

FACT FILE

- Border collies are a breed of herding dog descended from droving dogs used in the English–Welsh and English–Scottish borders. They were originally bred to work with sheep and other livestock but are also popular pets.

- Many of the best Border collies today can trace their lineage back to two dogs. Old Hemp was a champion in the late 1800s and won sheepdog trials all his life, never being beaten by another dog. He was tough on sheep and didn't like strangers. Old Kep was bred in the early 1900s, and he was much friendlier with people.

- Border collies are very intelligent – possibly the most intelligent dogs in the world.

- They have loads of energy and like lots and lots of exercise.

- They are happiest when they have a job to do. They like to work with a handler.

- The most common colour is black and white (like Rose and Izzy).

- Working Border collies respond to the human voice or whistles at long distances. When working with sheep, a trained sheepdog can do the work of three people.

- Border collies can also make good search-and-rescue dogs in mountain and moorland areas.

- Border Collies are very good at obedience and agility competitions as they are so fast and supple. One Border collie,

Gin, appeared with his owner, Kate, on British television in the finals of *Britain's Got Talent* and amazed viewers with his dog dancing (a form of obedience).

- A Border collie named Striker holds the current Guinness World Record for a dog winding down a car window – in 11.34 seconds!

LABRADOR RETRIEVERS

FACT FILE

- Labrador retrievers are a type of gun dog, used to retrieve (bring back) birds and animals shot for sport, but they make excellent pets and are one of the most popular breeds of dog in the world.

- They were first bred on the island of Newfoundland in Canada and were used by fishermen to help with pulling nets in from the water – the dog swims out and grabs the floating corks on the end of the nets and brings them in.

- They are quite big dogs. An average male weighs 30–36 kg. They love eating so they sometimes eat too much and get a bit too fat.

- Their coats are usually either black, yellow or what is called chocolate (medium to dark brown).

- Their coats are water-repellent so they don't get cold if they go in the water in the winter. They also have webbed toes so they are great swimmers.

- They are gentle, clever, good-natured dogs and are particularly good with children.

- They have very soft mouths – a Labrador can carry an egg in its mouth without breaking it!

CAUTION

It's hard to meet – or read about – a Border collie and not want one for yourself. They are beautiful, intelligent dogs. But this breed isn't for everyone. Nor are Labradors. Pearl and Clementine are magnificent dogs, but they might not be the right breed of dog for you.

If you are thinking of getting a dog, do talk to breeders, vets and other owners and make sure that you get the right one for you, and for your lifestyle. Border collies can be very difficult – there are lots of other breeds of dog to choose from.

Good rescue centres and dog breeders will always ask you lots of questions about your home and how much time you have available before they will let you have a dog. If they don't, you should go elsewhere.

You should always get a dog from a

registered breeder, or from an official rescue centre. Never go to a pet shop as their puppies may have come from puppy farmers – breeders out to make a quick profit who may not care about the health and welfare of their dogs.

For further information on dogs and dog ownership in the UK

The Kennel Club

www.thekennelclub.org

The Kennel Club was founded in 1873 and aims to "promote in every way the general improvement of dogs". They can provide lots of information and advice on dog welfare, health, training and breeding. They can also put you in touch with registered breeders of different kinds of dog. The breeders on their register sign up to recommended breeding guidelines.

The RSPCA

If you suspect a dog is being ill-treated or the owners need some help in knowing what their dog needs – for example, a Border collie would find it almost intolerable being shut in a flat on its own all day – call the RSPCA, and they will be able to offer advice, or will call round to see the dog. They also offer lots of advice for dog owners, including on buying a puppy and finding the right breed for you.

www.rspca.org.uk

24-hour cruelty and advice line: 0300 1234 999

Border Collie Rescue

This registered charity takes in, cares for, rehabilitates, retrains and re-homes Border collies and working sheepdogs. They also provide lots of advice and information about the breed. They are based in the UK, but they have contact links to animal rescue groups in 127 different countries.

www.bordercollierescue.org

Read on for a sneak peek at another of
Jon Katz's wonderful real-life stories . . .

THE TOTALLY TRUE STORY OF

DEVON

The Naughtiest Dog in the World

INTRODUCTION

This is a true story.

I love my dogs, and life with dogs is – for me – very rewarding. Dogs love purely and powerfully and without complications, and I feel so lucky to be able to share my life with them.

Devon is the Border collie star of this book and I hope you will enjoy meeting him as much as I enjoyed writing about him. This book first appeared as a longer book for adult readers, but when I travelled around with the book and my dogs (they came too, of course), we met lots of young people who wanted to know about them, and parents who asked if I could write the book again for their children to read.

This book is the result.

And my dogs (*almost* all of them) have loved children. Only Devon wasn't sure at first. But if you read his story, you will understand more about Devon – and about the challenge he brought to me in a very special dog year . . .

Jon Katz

CHAPTER ONE

One Man and His Dogs

It was morning in the Katz household and Jon, who worked as a writer, was just waking up. His dark hair rested on the pillow, and his glasses on the bedside table twinkled in the early morning sunlight.

Downstairs, Julius and Stanley, the family's two dogs, snoozed happily too. Their ears twitched, their paws shifted position now and then – and sometimes they let out a rumble of doggy snores.

Julius and Stanley were Labradors – big dogs

with silky golden coats the colour of butter, floppy ears and long wagging tails. They had lived with Jon and his wife, Paula, for a long time now and they all loved each other more than anything.

Jon had brought Julius home when he was just a puppy. "I've got a surprise for you!" he'd told Emma, his daughter, holding the wriggling doggy bundle out to the little girl, smiling at the puzzled frown on her face.

Emma had looked amazed as she'd moved her head close to Julius's.

Looking up at the shrieking girl, Julius had blinked, stuck out his long tongue and licked her nose. Jon had patted the puppy's head, and Julius had licked him too. They looked at each other for a moment, and somehow both of them had known at once that they would be friends.

A year later, his cousin Stanley had arrived. He came from the same breeder as Julius, and looked almost identical to the older dog when *he*'d moved in.

This tiny new puppy had melted Jon's heart straight away, though he had wondered whether

Julius would take to the newcomer. However, Stanley had soon won him over, and within a couple of days the two dogs loved each other and their new family as much as Jon and his family loved them.

It was now seven years since Stanley had joined the family. He and Julius were much bigger – and still the best of friends. Julius was eight years old and Stanley seven, but sometimes they behaved as if they were much older! They were both lazy dogs: all they wanted to do most of the time was rest! Sometimes Stanley would summon up the energy to chase a ball or have a swim in a pond, but apart from that the Labradors' days proceeded at a nice, comfortable, relaxed pace and they were happy with their quiet life!

Jon came downstairs for a glass of water and looked in on the dogs, waking them. As he went back upstairs, they followed him for their morning cuddle. Jon smiled, as he did every time he looked at his calm and loving pets, thinking for the millionth time how lucky he was to have them.

Dog Report

Name:	Julius
Age:	Eight
Breed:	Golden Labrador
Lives:	With Jon and Paula, in New York
Friends:	Everybody! But especially Jon and Stanley
Likes:	Sleeping, lots of hugs, rawhide chews, dinner, walks, sniffing interesting smells, staring at the tops of mountains for hours
Doesn't like:	Rainy days (he's allergic to rainy days), the sea (he's allergic to sea water)

Dog Report

Name:	Stanley
Age:	Seven
Breed:	Golden Labrador
Lives:	With Jon and Paula, in New York
Friends:	Everybody! But especially Jon and Julius
Likes:	Sleeping, lots of hugs, biscuits, dinner, chasing balls, sniffing interesting smells, swimming in ponds, playing tug-of-war with rope toys
Doesn't like:	Rainy days

A typical day for Jon, Julius and Stanley:

Getting up

Neither dog moves a muscle until Jon is awake, then they slither into his bed for a big furry family cuddle. Wet noses and the odd lick are normal! After Jon is up, they sit quietly and attentively under the kitchen table, staring at their food bowls. *If we stare hard enough and long enough, will our food magically appear?* they wonder!

Early walk

This is a leisurely stroll of about half an hour through the local neighbourhood. Julius and Stanley want to sniff *everything*. No shrub or rock is missed and nothing can distract them when they smell something particularly interesting. The walks are peaceful, and they meet lots of dog buddies, friends and admirers. Everyone likes Julius and Stanley and the local children wave at them from bikes and car windows.

Note: Labradors are supposed to be hunting dogs – outdoor working dogs – but Julius and Stanley have never been keen on rain or snow. If the weather is nasty, they have mastered a hundred-metre dash to the nearest tree, and then they want to go back inside. This suits Jon nicely – he's not keen on walking in the rain either!

Snack time

This is two big rawhide chews with a layer of peanut butter in between. Jules and Stanley carry these treats into the garden and settle down for a good gnaw. This kind of thing can be pretty tiring for a dog and they need a good long rest afterwards, sometimes rousing themselves from their nap to bark at a passing dog. Mostly not.

Daytime

Jon works from home as a writer, which means he gets to spend *lots* of time with Stanley and Julius. It's a good thing they all get along so well! He works in his study; if it's rainy, the two dogs come in and act as footrests, both tucked underneath his desk, one on the left, one on the right; otherwise they nap in the sun. The dogs are clever, knowing exactly when Jon has an important deadline and needs to be left in peace.

Afternoon walk

This is maybe a mile or so, but no one's in any hurry – it's a gentle stroll.

More snacks

Jon knows that he shouldn't give his boys snacks, but he can't resist offering them rawhide chews, pigs' ears and dog biscuits . . .

Dinner

Julius and Stanley like this time of day! But it doesn't take them long to scoff down their food.

Bedtime

As night falls, so the Labs settle down on their

beds for a final snack and then fall into a deep, unmoving sleep.

Later, out on their morning walk, Julius and Stanley padded along the familiar pavements, totally contented. After a while Stanley nipped Jon's bottom to get his attention. He wanted Jon to throw his ball for him to go and catch.

He didn't need to do anything else: Jon knew exactly what he wanted and threw the ball into the grass ahead. Stanley yapped happily and raced after it.

We could all do this in our sleep, Jon thought as they strolled along. They were almost like a school of fish, the three of them, veering first in one direction, then another. They turned corners at the same time, knew each other's moods and were happy sitting in silence together in various parks and gardens, sharing their lunch.

The three of them enjoyed their walk in the sun, little knowing that things were about to change for ever. And the change was coming on four legs . . .

CHAPTER TWO

The Arrival of Devon

A few days later, Jon got a phone call. He'd barely had time to say hello before the woman on the other end of the phone introduced herself as Deanne, a Border collie breeder. She had read one of Jon's books in which he'd mentioned how much he loved dogs, and had looked him up. Now she started talking very quickly and very loudly, and it took Jon a few moments to catch up with what she was saying . . .

"This dog *belongs* with you," Deanne told him.

"He's a special case. He needs special handling and I really think you're the right person for him . . ." She went on to tell him all about Devon, a Border collie she had bred. The dog had been trained by his owner to compete in obedience competitions, but he had stopped performing as well as he used to and wasn't winning anything any more. Devon's owners no longer wanted him and had given him back to Deanne. The poor little collie was feeling rejected and unloved – and he needed a good home.

Jon shook his head, even though Deanne, on the other end of the phone, couldn't see him. He was happy with his life here, he thought. He didn't think Paula would want any more dogs, Emma didn't live at home any more and *he* was happy with things the way they were too. He was just about to say no . . .

"Please, Jon," Deanne begged. "I just know you can give him the right home. He really needs someone who won't mind a bit of odd behaviour."

Jon looked through the window at Julius and

Stanley, who were napping in the sun. He thought of their peaceful, contented threesome. He already had two happy dogs who didn't demonstrate any "odd behaviour", and he had a very busy life. He knew what he *should* be saying, but he couldn't bring himself to actually utter the words. "OK," he told Deanne reluctantly. "I'll talk to Paula and Emma about it . . ."

Jon could hear the smile in her voice at his words! What had he done? he wondered. He didn't know very much about Border collies: he realized he'd better do some research . . .

What Jon *did* know about Border collies already was this:

- They were medium-sized dogs that looked a bit like small shaggy black-and-white wolves.
- They were very intelligent.
- They needed lots of space − vast areas to roam. Mountains and moors were ideal. He knew you didn't see a lot of mountains and

moorlands in a suburb outside a big city like his — you didn't see many Border collies, either.

- They had heaps of energy; they'd go crazy living shut up in a house all day while a family went out to work.

- They were developed as dogs to herd sheep.

- They loved to chase things — squirrels, rabbits, cars: anything that moved away from them. And they could run at blinding speeds.

Deanne called often over the next few days. This was a big decision for Jon and his family, and for Deanne, so they all needed to get as much information as they could to make sure the little Border collie found the right home. What Jon knew so far concerned *normal* Border collies. But the more information Deanne gave him, the more he realized that Devon was not a normal Border collie . . .

What Jon learned about Devon was this:

- He was two years old.
- He was very, very bright.
- He was well-bred but really highly strung.
- He had never lived in a house before, or with just one human.
- He was in big trouble and needed a new home – badly . . .

Jon ran this list of facts about Devon over and over in his mind. *Stop! Danger ahead!* he kept telling himself. But he just couldn't bring himself to say no to this dog in need. He sat at his desk and put his head in his hands. What should he do? This dog needed him.

He looked down at Julius and Stanley, who were lying under his feet. They were both well-behaved and loving, gentle with children and good-humoured. "Look at them," Jon said to himself. "I trained Julius and Stanley, so maybe I *can* take on Devon too. If I'm good with dogs, then

I should use my skills and give this needy young animal a loving home, shouldn't I?" *That's it!* he decided suddenly. "Boys," he told the Labradors triumphantly, "we're going to do it! We're going to give Devon a home."

Once his decision had been made, the time seemed to fly by. There was lots to do to prepare for the newest member of Jon's family, and in what seemed like no time at all he was heading for the airport to meet Devon. The lonely little Border collie was being flown east from Texas to start his new life with Jon just outside New York.

Jon was excited – he couldn't wait to meet Devon, but he couldn't lie: he was nervous too, and he did have a lot of worries. He still didn't know very much about the dog, apart from the fact that he needed a new home badly; he didn't even know what he looked like! Would he be up to the challenge? And what would Julius and Stanley think of the newcomer?

"Boys," Jon announced solemnly before he

left for the airport, "today's the day. I'm bringing another dog here – Devon. He might be a little wacky. Be patient."

Julius and Stanley looked at him fondly, their tails wagging. They could tell that their master was stressed about something, and they rubbed themselves patiently up against his legs in an attempt to calm him down. But neither they nor Jon had any idea how much trouble was heading towards them!

The airport was very busy and Devon's flight had been delayed. *Poor Devon*, Jon thought to himself as he paced up and down the arrivals hall. *The poor little guy's already been holed up in the plane near the noisy engines with everybody's heavy luggage – delays are the last thing he needs.* When he finally did get out of his crate, he'd probably be terrified. It was bedlam at the airport – luggage everywhere, people shouting, loudspeakers blaring, and crowds of passengers coming and going. Jon felt nervous himself as he stood there waiting for Devon – and he was *used* to airports. How would poor Devon feel?

Finally, after Jon had paced around the arrivals area for about an hour, he saw Devon's plane land outside on the runway. He caught the attention of a member of staff. "Is there a dog on that plane?" he asked. When the woman nodded, he smiled. In a matter of minutes Devon would be part of his family!

He stared fixedly at the arrivals gate in case he missed seeing Devon taking his first steps in New York. Finally, at 9p.m., two baggage handlers pulled a large blue dog-travelling crate noisily across the airport floor. Devon's crate was enormous! It had air holes along the sides and a metal grille over the front opening. On top rested an envelope with the dog's travel papers inside. Jon stepped forward excitedly. He had planned to reach into the crate, put on Devon's new blue collar and lead, and take him out to the car park as quickly as possible, away from the madness inside the airport. But as he looked into the crate, Jon realized that his plan was not going to come off as smoothly as he had thought!

There was a blanket scrunched up against the door of the cage and lots of shredded newspaper on the bottom. Jon took all this in carefully – but he couldn't actually see Devon himself! All he could make out was flashes of black and white circling round and round and round inside the crate. Devon was obviously desperate to get out!

"Devon," Jon called softly. "Devon, I'm going to open the door, boy. It's going to be OK." He had always talked to Julius and Stanley, and his Labradors seemed to understand him perfectly, but Devon clearly did not! As soon as Jon knelt to undo the latch, a blur of black and white fur shot past him into the crowd. The gate slammed open into Jon's face. "*Oof!*" he exclaimed as the force knocked him flat on his back.

Devon was out of sight before Jon could even scramble to his feet. When he did stand up again, he could see no sign of the dog, and only the shrieks and shouts from the crowds around the airport told Jon which way he was headed.

Devon was confused and frightened. He raced from one baggage carousel to another, then back again, desperately looking for a way out. Two baggage handlers and three policemen joined Jon in chasing after Devon, but whenever any of them got close to him, he turned and dashed in the other direction, vanishing into the crowds again.

Devon wheeled round,

and kept running

and running

and running.

Faster and faster.

He was out of control.

And he was also very frightened.

Jon was frightened too. The men trying to help him catch the little dog were getting impatient. "I think we need to call in the animal-control team," one of them grunted. "This crazy animal could bite a child or knock someone over – then there'll be trouble."

"I've seen dogs a lot less excited than this one bite people," another officer agreed.

Jon knew the men were right. A panicky dog in a strange place could be *very* dangerous. But he didn't know what to do. What if Devon dashed out of the doors and got loose in the car park or on the roads? He could be hit by a car . . .

Jon tried to stay calm. "Devon! Devon!" he called. There was no response. Devon wasn't slowing down for anyone.

Half an hour later, just as Jon was starting to wonder whether he *should* let the policemen call in the animal-control team, they finally managed to corner Devon. Jon knelt down in front of his new dog and took his first proper look at him.

Devon was beautiful, and Jon smiled down at him, despite the chaos he had just caused. The collie was sleek and black, with a pointed nose, a narrow white blaze on his forehead and a white chest. He was very skinny, and Jon could see that he had not enjoyed being cooped up in the travelling cage for hours. His fur was matted with sweat, and his body was hunched. He was panting heavily and his lovely dark eyes looked very, very sad. Jon knew at that moment that he had done the right thing – more than anything he needed to help this animal.

"Devon," he said softly, reaching out with one hand towards the scared dog. "Stay, Devon. Stay."

Jon had done a lot of reading about dogs like Devon over the past weeks, and all the books had said how important it was to make eye contact. In the wild, eye contact was how Border collies controlled sheep, and Jon knew that if he could catch Devon's eye now, the dog might obey him. Still speaking gently, he continued, "I'm your new friend. It's OK now. Stay, boy. I'm going to take you home." He repeated the words soothingly over and over again to try and calm the frightened young Border collie.

Jon slowly pulled a dog biscuit from his trouser pocket. He placed it on the ground and nudged it towards Devon.

The dog ignored the biscuit. The look in his sad eyes made Jon feel bad; it was as if he was saying, *Do you think I can be bribed that easily?* His eyes darted everywhere, carefully taking in everybody

– including Jon. Jon wondered if he was looking for another escape route, but for now the dog stayed where he was.

He decided to take his chance while Devon was calmer. "Stay," he said again. "Stay, Devon. It's OK." Devon raised his head and looked at the man carefully. Jon leaned forward and the collie allowed him to scratch him gently behind the ear.

Suddenly someone gave a loud shout nearby and Devon jerked away from Jon, scared by the noise. He tossed his head around, his eyes frightened.

Jon was worried that Devon might run off again, but he persisted: he needed to make friends with this dog. He carried on stroking his soft fur and then patted him on the shoulder. Very slowly and carefully he slipped on Devon's new collar and lead.

Devon stared up at Jon, looking him right in the eye. He looked as if he understood that this was his new master, and that they were going home together.

**Try these other fantastic titles from
Random House Children's Books . . .**

Christian the Lion

Based on the story of
Anthony Bourke and
John Rendall

*The true story of one lion's
search for a home . . .*

For sale: lion cubs,
in Harrods department store!

Imagine the surprise on shoppers' faces
when they see a pair of beautiful little lion
cubs for sale in London! Two friends, Ace
and John, can't bear to leave the male cub
behind, stuck in such a tiny cage.

So they take him home with them, and
they name him Christian. But it's not long
before the cheeky lion is getting into all
sorts of mischief and sticky situations!

Whatever will they do when Christian
changes from a cute and cuddly little cub
into a powerful and noble beast . . .?

ISBN: 978 1 862 30956 2